THE SMILE

MARIE VOIGT

OXFORD
UNIVERSITY PRESS

A smile is a beautiful gift.

From one face to another.

We **never**
run out of
smiles
to give.

No matter
how many
we've given
before.

A smile makes a sad face happy.

LAST BUS

And if you put a smile

on just one face . .

. . . before long

there will be

too

many

to

count.

We can put a smile
on faces that are
close . . .

. . . and faces that are far away.

let's
send some
smiles!
FOR AUNTIE

One World

A smile can be for faces
that we may never meet.

And a smile we give now . . .

. . . can bring a smile to others later.

Sometimes we can **help** people

to find smiles they have lost.

One World

Every smile

One World
ONE TV
+++SMILES TRAVEL THE WORLD+++

HELPER
HELPER
HELPER
HELPER

starts a wonderful journey.

Where will

your smile go?

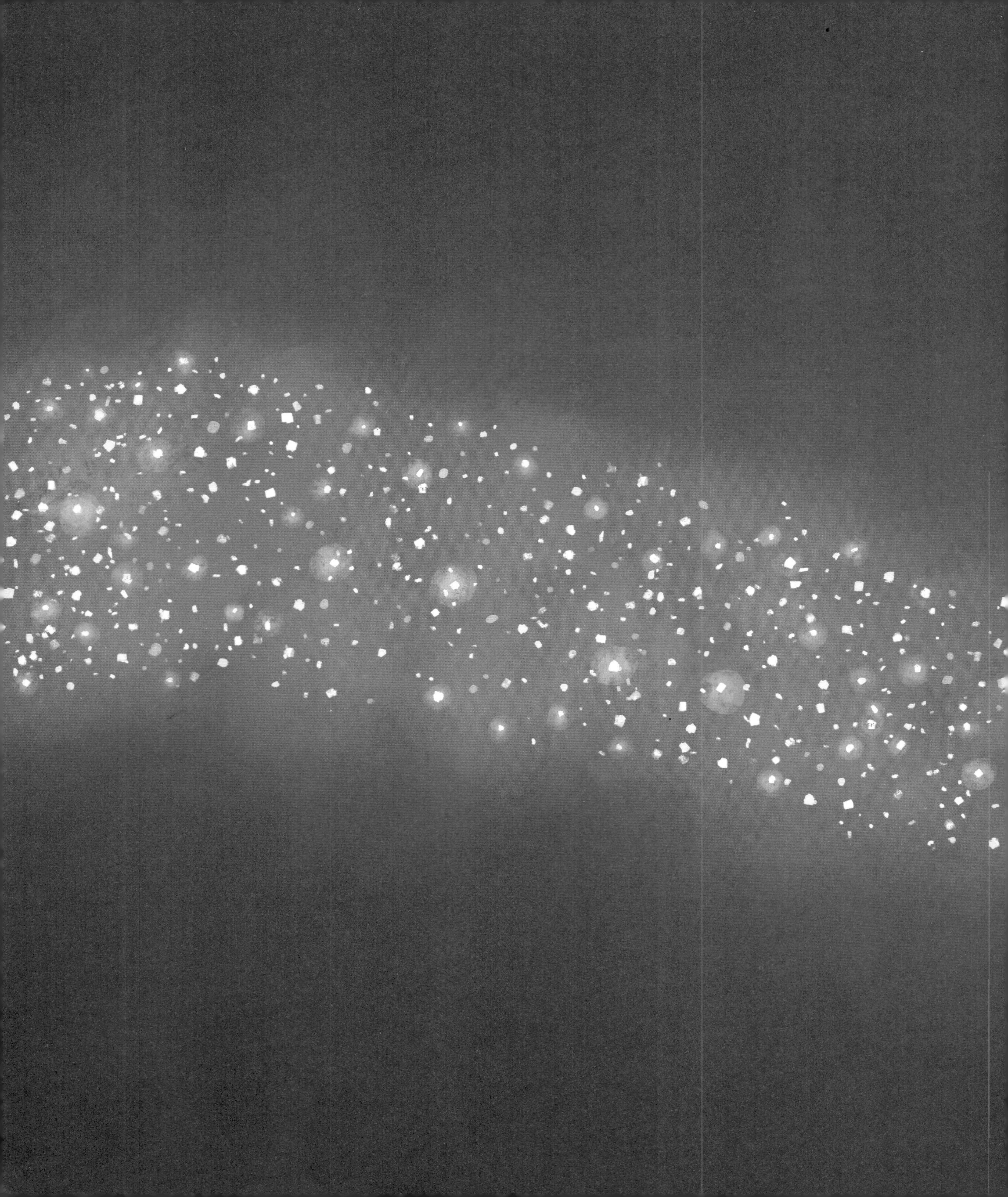